★ ★ ★ ★ ★ ★ ★ ★ ★ ★ ★ ★ ★

The American Journey

D1091480

Chapter Skills
Activities

GLENCOE
McGraw-Hill

New York, New York   Columbus, Ohio   Woodland Hills, California   Peoria, Illinois

To the Teacher

The American Journey Chapter Skills Activities booklet provides students with critical thinking and social studies skills practice that helps them apply information learned in the student text to situations in the real world. The activities show students how to use these basic skills and apply them to new situations and content. These activities will help students develop the skills to live and work in an ever-changing world.

Glencoe/McGraw-Hill

A Division of The McGraw·Hill Companies

Send all inquiries to:
Glencoe/McGraw-Hill
936 Eastwind Drive
Westerville, Ohio 43081

ISBN 0-02-821796-9

Printed in the United States of America

5 6 7 8 9 10 11 12   066   04 03 02 01 00 99

Customize Your Resources

No matter how you organize your teaching resources, Glencoe has what you need.

The **Teacher's Classroom Resources** for *The American Journey* provides you with a wide variety of supplemental materials to enhance the classroom experience. These resources appear as individual booklets in a carryall tote box. The booklets are designed to open flat so that pages can be easily photocopied without removing them from their booklet. However, if you choose to create separate files, the pages are perforated for easy removal. You may customize these materials using our file folders or tabbed dividers.

The individual booklets and the file management kit supplied in **Teacher's Classroom Resources** give you the flexibility to organize these resources in a combination that best suits your teaching style. Below are several alternatives:

- **Organize all resources by category**
  (all tests, all history themes activities, all cooperative learning activities, etc., filed separately)

- **Organize all resources by category and chapter**
  (all Chapter 1 activities, all Chapter 1 tests, etc.)

- **Organize resources sequentially by lesson**
  (activities, quizzes, readings, etc., for Chapter 1, Chapter 2, and so on)

Table of Contents

★ **Chapter Skills Activity 1**

Understanding the Parts of a Map

   Whether you are looking at a city bus map or a world climate map, you will notice certain features to help you understand the information the map provides. The map key, or legend, explains the meanings of special symbols, colors, or lines. The scale bar enables you to determine actual distances between points on the map. A compass rose shows the directions north, south, east, and west.

DIRECTIONS: This map shows Native American pueblos as well as modern cities and towns in a portion of New Mexico. Use the map to answer the following questions on a separate sheet of paper.

1. Is Santa Domingo a modern town or a pueblo?

2. Is Sandia closer to Albuquerque or Santa Fe?

3. In what direction would you travel to go from Santa Fe to Taos?

4. What pueblo could you visit if you traveled south from Albuquerque?

5. What is the approximate distance from Albuquerque to Santa Fe?

CRITICAL THINKING

6. Why do you think road maps distinguish between interstate highways and other highways?

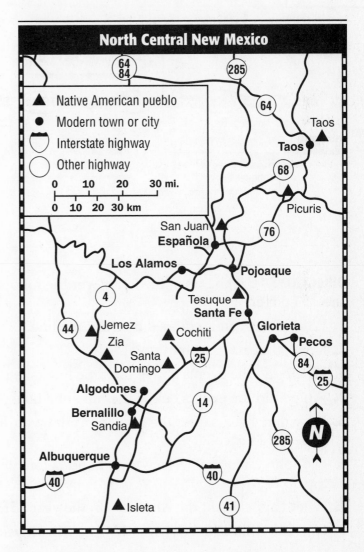

Activity   **DIRECTIONS:** Imagine that a visitor from another city is staying at your home. The visitor will speak to your class and needs directions from your home to your school. On a separate sheet of paper, create a map for the visitor to use to reach your school. Be sure to include a compass rose, map key, and map scale.

Name _____ Date _____ Class _____

Reading a Time Line

A time line lists events that occurred over a period of time. The number of years covered is called a time span, and the segments are called time intervals. A time line can show events in more than one place.

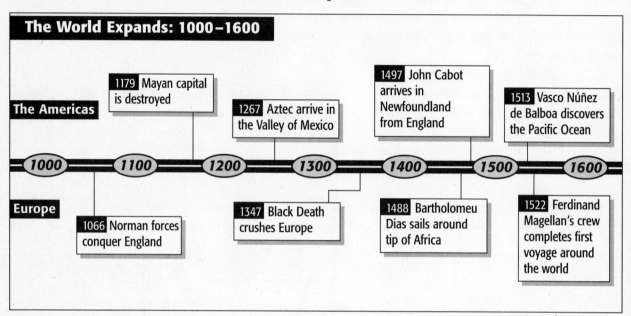

The World Expands: 1000–1600

The Americas

1179 Mayan capital is destroyed

1267 Aztec arrive in the Valley of Mexico

1497 John Cabot arrives in Newfoundland from England

1513 Vasco Núñez de Balboa discovers the Pacific Ocean

1000 — 1100 — 1200 — 1300 — 1400 — 1500 — 1600

Europe

1066 Norman forces conquer England

1347 Black Death crushes Europe

1488 Bartholomeu Dias sails around tip of Africa

1522 Ferdinand Magellan's crew completes first voyage around the world

DIRECTIONS: Use the time line to answer the following questions on a separate sheet of paper.

1. What time span is covered by this time line?
2. How far apart is each interval?
3. Where did the events above the time line take place?
4. Where did the events below the time line take place?
5. How many years after the Mayan capital was destroyed did the Aztec arrive in the Valley of Mexico?
6. Did John Cabot sail to Newfoundland before or after Bartholomeu Dias sailed around the tip of Africa?
7. What happened in the Americas in the year 1513?
8. **CRITICAL THINKING** Why was 1347 a difficult year in Europe?

Activity

DIRECTIONS: Create a family time line, using photos or drawings to show the birth dates of your family members.

Name _____ Date _____ Class _____

Reading a Bar Graph

A bar graph uses bars or columns of different lengths to show quantities. The horizontal axis along the bottom of the graph, and the vertical axis along the side of the graph, are labeled so you know what kind of information they show.

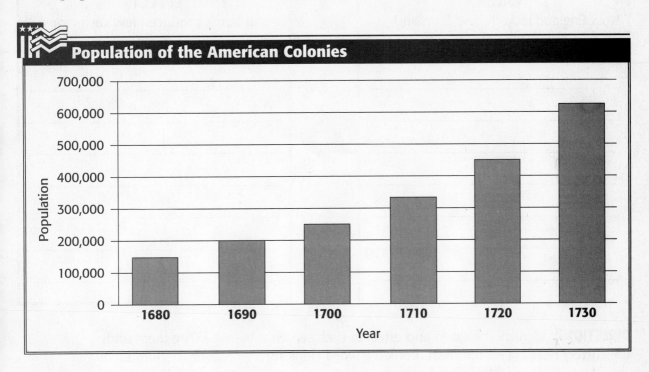

Population of the American Colonies

DIRECTIONS: Study the bar graph. Then answer the questions on a separate sheet of paper.

1. What is the subject of this bar graph?

2. What years are shown on the graph?

3. What was the population of the colonies in 1690?

4. In what year was the population of the colonies about 250,000?

5. About how much did the colonial population increase between 1700 and 1710?

6. How much did it increase between 1710 and 1720?

7. Between what years did the biggest increase occur?

8. **CRITICAL THINKING** What trend does the bar graph show?

Activity **DIRECTIONS:** Keep track of how many students are present in your class for one week. Make a bar graph showing attendance for each day of the week. Which day had the highest attendance? The lowest?

★ **Chapter Skills Activity 4**

Understanding Cause and Effect

An event or a condition that makes something happen is a *cause*. An *effect* is what happens as a result of the cause. For example:

CAUSE	EFFECT
New England lacked good farmland.	Small farms produced few cash crops.

DIRECTIONS: Identify the cause and effect in each sentence below. Write them under the correct heading on the chart. Look for word clues such as *because, resulted in, in order to, so that,* and *therefore* to help you determine causes and effects.

1. Because of differences in natural features, climate, and soil, the economies of the New England, Middle, and Southern Colonies developed differently.

2. The British Parliament passed laws controlling the flow of goods between Great Britain and the colonies to make sure that only Great Britain profited from trade.

3. The rivalry between Great Britain and France over land and resources in North America eventually led to armed conflict.

4. Because farming was so profitable in the South, agriculture rather than industry formed the backbone of the Southern economy.

5. The French were more tolerant of Native American culture than the British. Many Native Americans therefore sided with the French in their conflict with the British.

Activity **DIRECTIONS:** On a separate sheet of paper, make a cause-and-effect diagram. List a cause like, **I did not get home from school in time to do my homework before dinner,** in a box at the top of the sheet. Then, in boxes below the cause, list the possible effects of the cause. If some of the effects have additional effects, list them also.

Name _____ Date _____ Class _____

★ **Chapter Skills Activity 5**

Distinguishing Fact From Opinion

Facts can be verified and checked for accuracy. Opinions express beliefs and cannot be proved or disproved. Expert opinions on a topic, such as a doctor's opinion on health, may be more reliable than other opinions. Words and phrases such as *I believe, I think, probably, might, could, should, best, worst,* and *greatest* help identify opinions.

DIRECTIONS: Read the statements. If the statement is a fact, write **F** and explain how you could check its accuracy. If it is an opinion, write **O** and underline words that suggest it is opinion.

_____ **1.** Members of the British Parliament should have considered more carefully the effect of their tax policies on the American colonists. _____

_____ **2.** The Stamp Act of 1765 required colonists to pay a tax on printed material. _____

_____ **3.** Patrick Henry's speeches before the Virginia House of Burgesses were the most stirring political speeches made in colonial America. _____

_____ **4.** I think taxes are as important in modern politics as in colonial politics. _____

_____ **5.** Even after the repeal of the Townshend Acts, some colonial leaders continued to urge the colonists to resist British rule. _____

_____ **6.** John Dickinson's "Letters from a Farmer in Pennsylvania to the Inhabitants of the British Colonies" became a widely read publication. _____

_____ **7.** If the British Parliament had limited its powers to regulating colonial trade, the colonists probably would not have rebelled. _____

_____ **8.** George Washington was the only military leader capable of leading the Continental Army. _____

_____ **9.** Thomas Paine referred to King George III as a "royal brute" in his pamphlet *Common Sense.* _____

Activity **DIRECTIONS:** Write a letter to the principal of your school that identifies a school problem and suggests a solution. Use a highlighter to identify the opinion statements in your letter. Then list additional facts to support your opinion.

★ Chapter Skills Activity 6

Reading a Military Map

A military map shows where battles occurred. Symbols show troop movements, victories, and defeats. A military map may also show important geographic features that influence military strategy.

DIRECTIONS: Use the map to answer these questions.

1. In which three states did most of the fighting in 1776–1777 take place?

_____

_____

2. What symbol is used to indicate American troop movements?

_____

3. From what direction did the British troops march on Philadelphia?

_____

4. Which side won victories at Trenton and Princeton?

_____

5. From looking at the map, which side do you think had a larger navy? How can you tell?

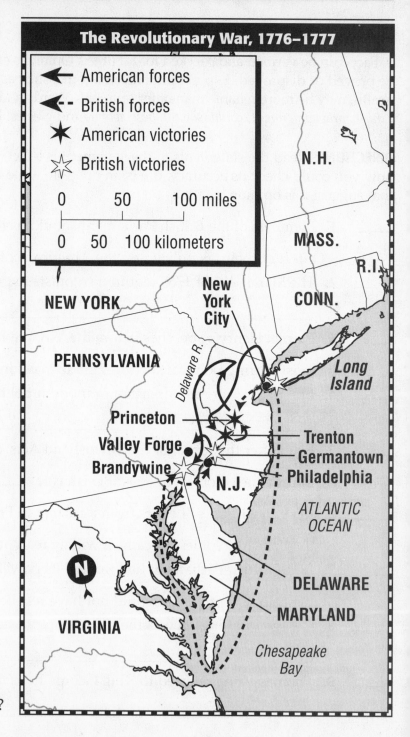

The Revolutionary War, 1776–1777

◄— American forces

◄-- British forces

✶ American victories

☆ British victories

0   50   100 miles

0   50   100 kilometers

N.H.

MASS.

R.I.

NEW YORK

New York City

CONN.

PENNSYLVANIA

Long Island

Delaware R.

Princeton

Valley Forge

Brandywine

Trenton

Germantown

Philadelphia

N.J.

ATLANTIC OCEAN

N

DELAWARE

MARYLAND

VIRGINIA

Chesapeake Bay

Activity

DIRECTIONS: Imagine you are a Revolutionary War soldier, either on the British or the American side. On a separate sheet of paper, write several diary entries as a soldier might have written them. Use the map to identify places and troop movements for each diary entry.

★ **Chapter Skills Activity 7**

Making Comparisons

Making a comparison involves looking at similarities and differences.

DIRECTIONS: While James Madison attended the Constitutional Convention, he corresponded with Thomas Jefferson, in France, about the importance of including a bill of rights. Compare the similarities and differences in their points of view. Then answer the questions on a separate sheet of paper.

... Let me add that a bill of rights is what the people are entitled to against every government on earth. ...

I think our governments will remain virtuous for many centuries. ... Above all things I hope the education of the common people will be attended to, convinced that on their good sense we may rely with the most security for the preservation of a proper degree of liberty.

Thomas Jefferson

My own opinion has always been in favor of a bill of rights ... At the same time ... I have not viewed it in an important light—

Wherever the real power lies in a government, there is the danger of oppression. In our governments the real power lies in the majority of the community, and the invasion of private rights is to be feared <u>chiefly</u>, not from acts of government contrary to the sense of its constituents, but from acts in which the government is the mere instrument of the majority of the constituents. ...

James Madison

1. Explain in your own words the point of view expressed by Thomas Jefferson.
2. Explain in your own words the point of view expressed by James Madison.
3. On what point did Jefferson and Madison agree?
4. Which individual expressed greater confidence in the ability of the American people to govern wisely?
5. Which individual believed that actions taken by the people themselves could pose a threat to individual liberties?

Activity **DIRECTIONS:** Imagine that a family member has offered to give you a compact disc player for your birthday. You are allowed to pick out the kind you would like. Choose two different brands and make a chart comparing the two compact disc players. Consider such things as price, size, sound quality, and so on. Which one would you choose? Why?

★ **Chapter Skills Activity 8**

Reading a Flowchart

A flowchart can make a sequence of events or the steps in a process easy to follow. To read a flowchart, look for numbers or arrows that indicate sequence.

DIRECTIONS: Filling in the Blanks This flowchart shows the sequence of events in the conflict between the United States and France that led to undeclared war between the two nations. Analyze the information in the chart. Then answer the questions below.

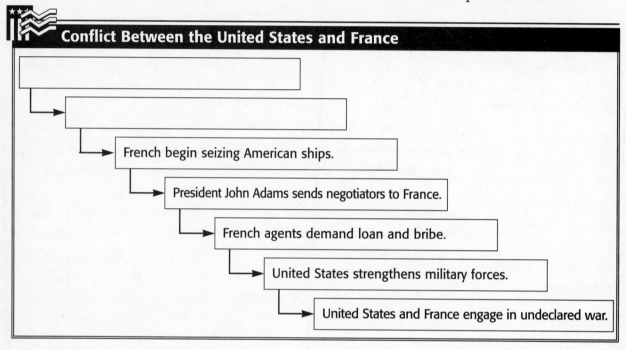

Conflict Between the United States and France

French begin seizing American ships.

President John Adams sends negotiators to France.

French agents demand loan and bribe.

United States strengthens military forces.

United States and France engage in undeclared war.

1. What is the title of this flowchart? _____

2. What actions taken by the French eventually provoked armed conflict between France

and the United States? _____

_____

3. What evidence is there that President Adams wanted to avoid war with France?

_____

4. What did the United States do after its efforts to negotiate with France failed?

_____

5. CRITICAL THINKING What information from the chapter could you add to the beginning

of the flowchart? _____

★ **Chapter Skills Activity 9**

Writing a Journal

In a history journal, you can record your reactions to events taking place around you or to people and events that you have read about. Sometimes, asking yourself questions and exploring your own reactions can help you understand historical events or situations better.

DIRECTIONS: Completing a Chart The first verse of "The Star-Spangled Banner" appears below. Review the section in your textbook that explains the circumstances that led Francis Scott Key to write this poem. Then explore your response to the poem.

> Oh! say, can you see, by the dawn's early light,
> What so proudly we hailed at the twilight's last gleaming?
> Whose broad stripes and bright stars thro' the perilous fight,
> O'er the ramparts we watched were so gallantly streaming?
> And the rockets' red glare, the bombs bursting in air,
> Gave proof thro' the night that our flag was still there.
> Oh! say, does that star-spangled banner yet wave
> O'er the land of the free and the home of the brave?

The Star-Spangled Banner

Unfamiliar words and their meanings	Important images in poem

Why poem became national anthem	Your feelings and thoughts about poem

Name _____ Date _____ Class _____

Reading a Diagram

DIRECTIONS: Filling in the Blanks Canals can link bodies of water that are at different levels. Locks make it possible for ships to travel from one water level to another by raising or lowering the ships. This diagram shows how a lock works. Study the diagram and then answer the questions below.

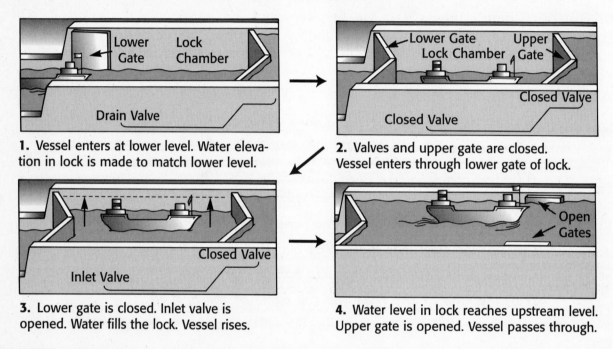

1. Vessel enters at lower level. Water elevation in lock is made to match lower level.

2. Valves and upper gate are closed. Vessel enters through lower gate of lock.

3. Lower gate is closed. Inlet valve is opened. Water fills the lock. Vessel rises.

4. Water level in lock reaches upstream level. Upper gate is opened. Vessel passes through.

1. The first illustration shows a boat entering a canal lock. Is the lower gate open or closed? _____

2. What is happening to the water level in the lock in illustration 3?

_____

3. Is the water level in the lock chamber higher in illustration 1 or 4?

_____

4. What happens after the water level in the lock is the same as the water level outside the lock? _____

_____

Activity **DIRECTIONS:** Diagrams can help make a process clearer that would be difficult to explain with words alone. Pick a simple household task—opening a soup can, for example—and make a diagram that explains the process.

★ **Chapter Skills Activity 11**

Analyzing Primary Sources

DIRECTIONS: Filling in the Blanks The excerpt that follows is from an eyewitness account of the inauguration of Andrew Jackson in 1829. Read the excerpt and answer the questions below.

> . . . Some one came and informed us the crowd before the President's house was so far lessened that they thought we might enter. This time we effected our purpose. But what a scene did we witness! . . .
>
> . . . Ladies and gentlemen only had been expected at this levee, not the people en masse. But it was the people's day, and the people's President, and the people would rule. . . . I fear, enlightened freemen as they are, they will be found, as they have been found in all ages and countries where they get the power in their hands, that of all tyrants, they are the most ferocious, cruel, and despotic. The noisy and disorderly rabble in the President's house brought to my mind descriptions I had read of the mobs in Tuileries and at Versailles. I expect to hear the carpets and furniture are ruined; the streets were muddy, and these guests all went thither on foot.
> —Mrs. Samuel Harrison Smith,
> "The First Forty Years of Washington Society"

SOURCE: *The Heritage of America.* Commager, Henry Steele and Allan Nevins, ed. Little, Brown and Company. Boston, 1951.

1. When did the events described in the paragraph take place? _____

2. What events are described in the excerpt? _____

_____

3. Where did the events take place? _____

4. How does the author describe the mob of people? _____

_____

5. CRITICAL THINKING What can you conclude about the person who wrote this account? Was she a member of the upper or lower social class at the time? Explain how you

reached your conclusion. _____

Activity **DIRECTIONS:** Use the editorial page of a local newspaper to find a letter to the editor or an opinion from a columnist related to a recent event. Look for an account that the writer witnessed. Write a brief critique of the account. How reliable do you think the account is? What can you tell about the writer from the account?

★ **Chapter Skills Activity 12**

Understanding Latitude and Longitude

The grid lines on maps and globes are lines of latitude and longitude. Lines of latitude, also called *parallels*, are horizontal. Lines of longitude, also called *meridians*, are vertical. The exact location of any place on Earth can be given in coordinates— the point at which parallels and meridians intersect.

DIRECTIONS: Filling in the Blanks This map shows the route that clipper ships took to sail from eastern cities to California. Until the Panama Canal opened in 1914, the long journey around the tip of South America was the fastest way for passengers and goods to reach the new settlements on the West coast.

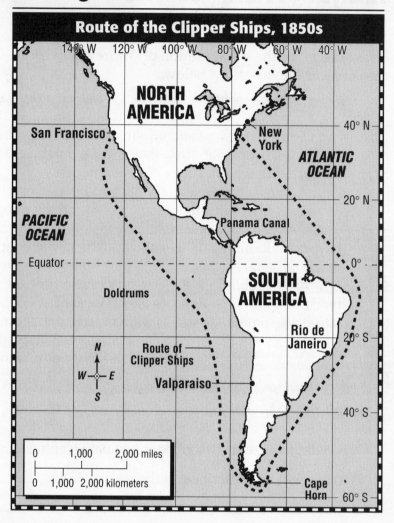

Route of the Clipper Ships, 1850s

1. What are the approximate coordinates of San Francisco?

_____

2. What are the approximate coordinates of Rio de Janeiro? _____

3. About how many degrees north of the Equator is the Panama Canal? _____

4. About how many degrees south of the Equator is Cape Horn? _____

5. In a region near the Equator, light breezes alternate with sudden thunderstorms. These unusual weather conditions make sailing very difficult. What is this region called?

_____

Activity **DIRECTIONS:** Make a longitude and latitude puzzle. Use an atlas to plan a road trip to several different locations. Identify the stops on the trip with coordinates of longitude and latitude. Then exchange your puzzle with a classmate. Identify the places you will stop by name.

★ Chapter Skills Activity 13

Reading a Circle Graph

A circle graph is useful in comparing parts of a whole. The entire circle stands for the whole thing, or 100 percent of something. The sections represent the parts that make up the whole.

DIRECTIONS: Filling in the Blanks Use the four circle graphs below to answer the questions that follow.

1. What do the four graphs show?

_____

_____

_____

2. What percentage of people lived in rural areas in 1830?

_____

In 1860? _____

3. During which two decades did the number of people living in urban areas increase by about five percent?

_____

_____

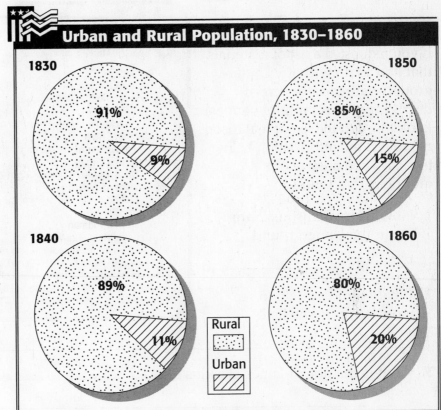

Urban and Rural Population, 1830–1860

1830 91% 9%

1850 85% 15%

1840 89% 11%

1860 80% 20%

Rural

Urban

_____

4. What conclusion can you draw from the graphs about the relationship of rural dwellers

to urban dwellers from 1830 to 1860? _____

_____

Activity

DIRECTIONS: Make a circle graph to show the composition of your class. Count the number of males and females in the class and determine what percentage of the class each group represents. Draw conclusions about the composition of your class.

★ **Chapter Skills Activity 14**

Using a Computerized Card Catalog

A computerized card catalog can help you find a specific book or a variety of resources about a research topic. Usually, you begin by requesting a particular kind of search, such as a title search, a search by author's name, or a search of materials on a general subject. Once you have located an item you want, you can check its call number, availability, or other information such as the date of publication for the source.

DIRECTIONS: Filling in the Blanks
If you requested a list of materials that had to do with the Underground Railroad, the screen display on the right might appear. Look through the list of materials as well as the information below the list. Then answer the questions that follow.

```
SEATTLE PUBLIC LIBRARY              10:56 am
Public Access Catalog

Your Search: Underground railroad.

   AUTHOR/TITLE                                    DATE
 1. Mitchell, William M.                           1970
       The Underground Railroad,
 2. Adler, David A.                                1992
       A picture book of Harriet Tubman /
 3. Cosner, Sharon.                                1991
       The underground railroad /
 4. Hamilton, Virginia.                            1993
       Many thousand gone: African Americans from slavery to freedom /
 5. Haskins, James, 1941–                          1993
       Get on board: the story of the Underground Railroad /
 6. Burns, Bree.                                   1992
       Harriet Tubman /
 7. Connell, Kate, 1954–                           1992
       Tales from the underground railroad /
 ★★★★★ 46 Items UNSORTED – Page 1 – More on Next Screen ★★★★★
 Enter an item number for more detail:
 SO=Start Over, B=Back, SL=Sort List, ?=Help, <enter>=Next Screen
 SB=Save Bib, L=Limit Search, SBLIST=Save Bib List
```

1. How many items in all are about the Underground Railroad? _____

2. What would you do to see more items on the list?

_____

3. What is the title of James Haskins's book? _____

_____

4. What would you do to get more information about Haskins's book? _____

_____

5. Suppose you are looking at a screen display about Haskins's book. Now you want to obtain information about another book on the list. What would you type first?

_____

6. **Media Literacy** You have finished looking at the books about the Underground Railroad. Now you decide to see a list of all materials the library has about Harriet

Tubman. What do you type first? _____

Activity **DIRECTIONS:** Use the electronic card catalog to locate books on a subject that interests you. Create a screen similar to the one above. Then locate the books on the list and write a brief description of a book on your catalog card.

★ **Chapter Skills Activity 15**

Recognizing Bias

It is sometimes easy to recognize bias. An author states an opinion and tells you it is an opinion. Sometimes you may need to figure out whether an author's account of events is biased. To recognize bias, ask yourself questions such as: Does the author consider more than one point of view? Why did the author write the piece? How might the author's background influence his or her viewpoint?

DIRECTIONS: Filling in the Blanks In the passage below Nellie Thomas describes the lives of slaves on her grandfather's plantation in South Carolina. Read the passage and answer the questions that follow on a separate sheet of paper.

. . . Grandfather held his slaves as part of his official family. He owned them in families and encouraged the making of family ties among them. By these natural methods of economic conservation there were before very long many Negroes in the "quarters." As Grandfather was his own overseer, he gave his personal attention and supervision to every detail of his business and looked closely after the comfort, health, and moral well-being of his slaves.

Grandfather's discipline with his slaves was mild, but exceedingly firm. There was no rebellion or even an undercurrent of dissatisfaction against his rule. They all obeyed him implicitly. I think the secret of his success and his hold on his employees was the absolute system and order that marked the program of plantation work. . . . Amid such conditions—conditions that were their right—the slaves were happy and cheerful and worked willingly and enthusiastically. . . .

The commissary where supplies were kept resembled a country store. Every Wednesday at sundown the heads of all the Negro families gathered at this store to get their weekly allowance of provisions. Each allotment had been weighed and measured in advance and was ready to be delivered. It was an interesting sight. Each Negro received his portion, hoisted it to his shoulder, and went off, singing, to his cabin. . . .

SOURCE: *The Heritage of America.* Commager, Henry Steele and Allan Nevins, ed. Little, Brown and Company.

1. According to the author, how did the slaves on her grandfather's plantation feel about their lives and their work?

2. What evidence does the author give to support her picture of the slaves' lives?

3. Does the author present a positive or negative view of slavery?

4. How might the author's background have influenced her beliefs about slavery?

5. CRITICAL THINKING What makes you recognize that the author's viewpoint is biased?

★ **Chapter Skills Activity 16**

Using a CD-ROM

A CD-ROM can store speeches, music, photographs, and other visual images as well as words. If you were using a CD-ROM encyclopedia to do research on John F. Kennedy, for example, you could read an article about him, listen to one of his speeches, and see a news clip of his inauguration.

DIRECTIONS: Filling in the Blanks Most CD-ROM encyclopedias have certain features in common. They have toolbars, or rows of buttons, to help you search through the disc's contents. They also feature "dialog boxes" in which you enter information about your topic. Look at the displays below, and then answer the questions that follow.

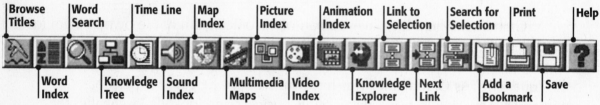

| Browse Titles | Word Search | Time Line | Map Index | Picture Index | Animation Index | Link to Selection | Search for Selection | Print | Help |

| Word Index | Knowledge Tree | Sound Index | Multimedia Maps | Video Index | Knowledge Explorer | Next Link | Add a Bookmark | Save |

1. Which button or buttons would you click on to find out whether there are any maps

of Civil War battles on a CD-ROM encyclopedia? _____

2. Which button would you click on to find out whether there are any recordings of

Abraham Lincoln's Gettysburg Address? _____

3. Which button would you click on to print a copy of an article? _____

Suppose you wanted to research Abraham Lincoln's beliefs about slavery. You could use the Word Search feature to find articles that have the words "Abraham Lincoln" and "slavery" in the same paragraph. The paragraphs are then displayed on the screen.

4. How would you search to find whether the countries of Europe assisted either side during the Civil War?

_____

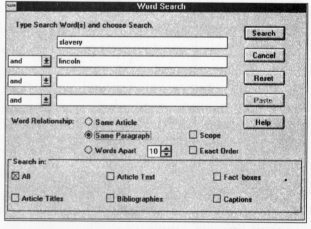

5. How would you search to find how many casualties there were at the Battle of

Gettysburg? _____

6. How would you search to find when African Americans began to serve in the

Union army? _____

★ **Chapter Skills Activity 17**

Identifying the Main Idea

Identifying main ideas as you read will help you grasp the flow of events in history. To identify the main idea of a passage, figure out the purpose of the passage. What picture is the author presenting? Look for important details and try to determine how they are related to each other.

DIRECTIONS: Recalling Facts Radical Reconstructionist Thaddeus Stevens made this proposal to Congress in 1867. Read the passage and answer the questions on a separate sheet of paper.

> Four million persons have just been freed from a condition of dependence. These are people, who, through no fault of their own, have no knowledge of business and do not even have the simplest elements of education. Few of them are mechanics and none of them are skilled manufacturers. They must necessarily, then, become the servants and victims of others unless they are, in some way, made independent of their neighbors. Should we keep them in a position where they have neither skills nor property, then it seems probable that their condition will become so desperate that the war of the races which so many fear, may well take place.
>
> However, by giving them the land and the money with which to build a dwelling, we will make them independent of their old masters . . . ."

SOURCE: *The Congressional Globe*, 70th Congress, First Session, March 19, 1867.

1. What is the subject of Thaddeus Stevens's address to Congress?

2. According to Stevens, what obstacles make it difficult or impossible for former slaves to achieve real independence? What details does Thaddeus Stevens give to describe the conditions of former slaves?

3. What does Stevens warn might happen if the situation of former slaves is not improved?

4. What is the main idea of Stevens's address to Congress?

5. **CRITICAL THINKING** Suppose that you participated in Reconstruction efforts to help newly freed African Americans become independent. You have written an editorial or given a speech on the subject. What would your main idea be? What are some important details you could use to support your main idea?

★ Chapter Skills Activity 18

Reading a Special-Purpose Map

Special-purpose maps can show a variety of information in addition to political boundaries and physical features. Some special-purpose maps have information about population growth, economic activities, and natural resources. Others provide cultural or historic information.

DIRECTIONS:
Filling in the Blanks By 1890, Native American nations in the western United States had been forced to give up, or cede, most of their traditional lands and move to reservations. Use the map on the right to answer the following questions.

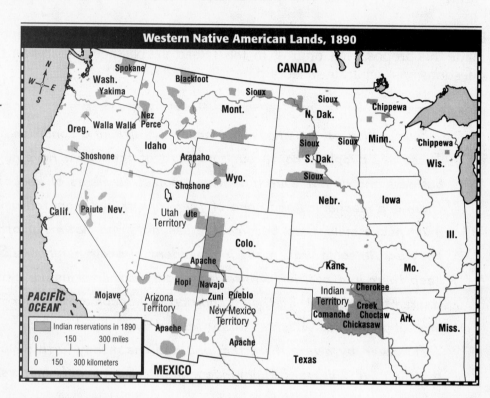

Western Native American Lands, 1890

1. What is the purpose of the map? _____

2. What state or territory had the largest area of Indian reservations in 1890? _____

3. Which Native American groups had reservations in Oregon? _____

CRITICAL THINKING

4. What conclusions can you draw from the labels "Arizona Territory," "Utah Territory," "New Mexico Territory," and "Indian Territory"? _____

_____

5. Do you think the Indian reservations were established for the benefit of the Native Americans? Refer to the map to help explain your answer. _____

_____

_____

★ **Chapter Skills Activity 19**

Reading a Time Zones Map

The world is divided into 24 different time zones. When you travel west, you subtract one hour for each time zone that you cross. When you travel east, you add one hour for each time zone that you cross.

DIRECTIONS: Filling in the Blanks Use the time zone map to answer the questions that follow.

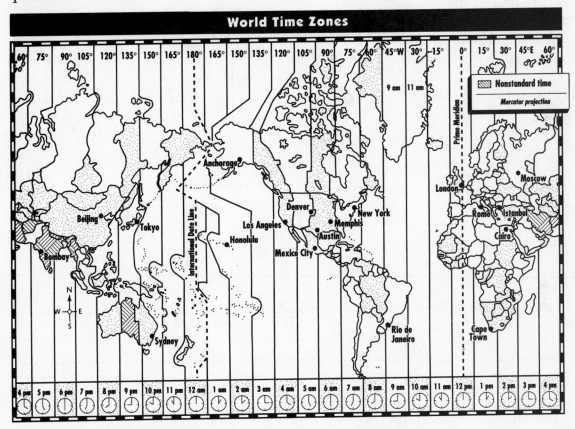

World Time Zones

1. When it is 3:00 P.M. in Mexico City, what time is it in New York? _____

   In London? _____ In Moscow? _____

2. How many hours earlier is it in Honolulu than in Memphis? _____

3. How many hours later is it in Rio de Janeiro than in Mexico City? _____

4. **CRITICAL THINKING** The boundaries of some time zones zigzag in certain areas. Why

   do you think this is so? _____

   _____

   _____

★ **Chapter Skills Activity 20**

Reading a Line Graph

Line graphs are often used to show changes that have taken place over time. To understand a line graph, first read the information along the bottom, or horizontal axis, and the left side, or vertical axis. To find out the value or amount at a particular time, locate the point on the line directly above a given year or time interval. Then determine the value of that point along the horizontal axis.

DIRECTIONS: Filling in the Blanks Study the line graph on the right. Then answer the questions that follow.

1. What is the subject of this

   line graph? _____

   _____

2. What is the period of time covered by this graph?

   _____

   _____

3. In what year was steel production about 4 million tons?

   _____

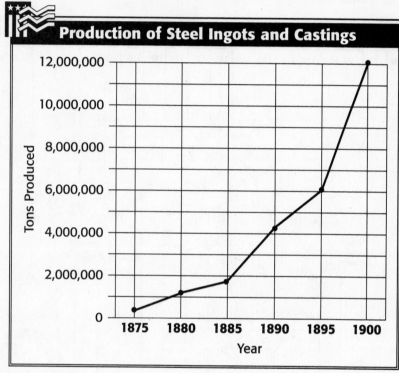

Production of Steel Ingots and Castings

Tons Produced / Year

4. About how many more tons of steel were produced in 1900 than in 1885? _____

5. During what five-year period did steel production increase the most? _____

6. **CRITICAL THINKING** What conclusions can you draw about the economy of the United

   States during the period of time covered by the graph? _____

   _____

Activity **DIRECTIONS:** Make a line graph to describe some aspect of your favorite sports team. Decide on the subject of your graph—touchdowns scored per football game, for example. Label one axis of your graph "games." Label the other axis "touchdowns." Then plot the correct points on the grid and connect the dots. How is your team doing?

★ **Chapter Skills Activity 21**

Interpreting a Political Cartoon

An editorial writer uses words to express an opinion about a political topic. A political cartoonist uses drawings to express a viewpoint. Most political cartoonists make use of caricature—exaggeration of a person's physical appearance—and symbols that represent countries, political organizations, or other entities or ideas, to get their point across.

DIRECTIONS: Filling in the Blanks
Study the political cartoon on the right. Then answer the questions that follow.

1. Who does the large figure in the cartoon

represent? _____
Who does the small figure represent?

_____

2. What is happening to the small figure

in the lemon squeezer? _____

3. Why do you think the figures are so different in size? _____

_____

4. What are some of the elements in the cartoon that tell you the large figure is wealthy?

_____

5. What is happening to the price of coal? _____

_____

6. How does the cartoonist feel about coal trusts? How does he probably feel about big

business in general? _____

_____

C is the Coal Trust, a greedy old bandit, Who squeezes the People. How long will they stand it?

HE'S MY LEMON

NOTICE.— COAL $15 PER TON, AND STILL RISING

COAL TRUST

COMMON PEOPLE

COPYRIGHT, 1902, BY W. R. HEARST.

F. Opper

SOURCE: Culver Pictures

DIRECTIONS: Draw a political cartoon that gives your opinion about an issue at your school. Be sure to use the techniques of political cartooning that you have just learned about.

★ **Chapter Skills Activity 22**

Developing Multimedia Presentations

Most presentations are more interesting and easier to follow if they include diagrams, photographs, videos, or sound recordings. Equipment you may have at home, plus classroom or library equipment and resources, can make it possible for you to develop interesting multimedia presentations.

DIRECTIONS: Completing the Media Plan Plan a multimedia presentation on a topic found in the chapter such as Matthew Perry's mission to Japan or the building of the Panama Canal. List three or four major ideas you would like to cover. Then think about how multimedia resources could enhance your presentation. Use the media center to do a preliminary survey of materials that may be available and list them on the chart. Use your imagination.

Topic: _____

Major Ideas: _____

_____

_____

Pictures, Photographs, or Diagrams	Videos	Animation	Sound Recordings

Activity **DIRECTIONS:** Create a multimedia presentation about some event in your neighborhood. Use the planning techniques that you practiced in the exercise above. Use as many multimedia materials as possible, including those that you create, such as photographs, drawings, charts, graphs, posters, music recordings, or videotapes. Share your multimedia presentation with your class.

★ **Chapter Skills Activity 23**

Outlining

Making an outline of written material can help you understand and remember main ideas and details. To outline material, look for section heads to help you identify main ideas. Then place details and subheads under the appropriate heads.

DIRECTIONS: Completing an Outline Complete the outline using Section 4 of Chapter 23. Refer to this section as you work. You may use a separate sheet of paper if necessary.

I. Preparing Americans to fight a war

   A. Creation of National War Labor Board

      1. _____

      2. _____

   B. Shortage of labor

      1. _____

      2. New opportunities for women and minorities

         a. _____

         b. _____

         c. _____

   C. Raising money for the war effort

      1. _____

      2. _____

   D. Mobilizing public support for war

      1. Committee on Public Information

         a. _____

         b. _____

         c. _____

II. Production of food and military supplies

   A. Creation of Food Administration

      1. _____

      2. _____

   B. Imposition of price controls

   C. Creation of War Industries Board

III. Impact of war on society

   A. _____

   B. _____

   C. Migration of African Americans

      1. _____

      2. _____

      3. _____

IV. Opposition to war

   A. Groups that opposed war

      1. _____

      2. _____

      3. _____

   B. Government treated opponents of war harshly

      1. _____

      2. _____

★ **Chapter Skills Activity 24**

Making Generalizations

Generalizations are judgments that are usually true based on the facts at hand. As you read, think about how historical facts are related to each other. Try to form generalizations, or conclusions drawn from facts. To make a valid generalization, you need sufficient information to support it.

DIRECTIONS: Identifying Valid and Invalid Generalizations Read the excerpt below. Identify each generalization that follows as *valid* or *invalid* based on the information in the passage.

The radio manufacturer occupied a less important seat than the automobile manufacturer on the prosperity bandwagon, but he had the distinction of being the youngest rider. You will remember that there was no such thing as radio broadcasting to the public until the autumn of 1920, but that by the spring of 1922 radio had become a craze—as much talked about as Mah Jong was to be the following year or cross-word puzzles the year after. In 1922, the sales of radio sets, parts, and accessories amounted to $60,000,000. People wondered what would happen when the edge wore off the novelty of hearing a jazz orchestra in Schenectady or in Davenport, Iowa, play "Mr. Gallagher and Mr. Shean." What actually did happen is suggested by the cold figures of total annual radio sales for the next few years:

1922–$ 60,000,000	1925–$430,000,000	1928–$650,550,000
1923–$136,000,000	1926–$506,000,000	1929–$842,548,000
1924–$358,000,000	1927–$425,600,000	(an increase over the 1922 figures of 1,400 percent!)

SOURCE: Allen, Frederick Lewis. *Only Yesterday and Since Yesterday: A Popular History of the 20s and 30s.* Bonanza Books. New York. 1986.

---

1. _____ The radio had a greater impact on the cultural life of Americans than the automobile.

2. _____ The popularity of the radio grew rapidly during the Jazz Age.

3. _____ With the exception of one year, radio sales increased each year over the previous year.

4. _____ Mah-jongg and crossword puzzles were fads that only lasted a short time.

5. CRITICAL THINKING What generalization can you make about the pursuit of leisure

activities during the 1920s based on the excerpt? _____

Activity   **DIRECTIONS:** Over a period of weeks, read the editorials in your local newspaper. Then write a list of generalizations about the newspaper's positions on several issues, such as politics, education, crime, or other issues that affect the United States, your state, or your community.

★ Chapter Skills Activity 25

Analyzing News Media

Some news stories report events objectively; others analyze and interpret them. When you read a news article, evaluate how objective it is. If the reporter does not seem to be fair, you need to look at other sources before making up your mind.

DIRECTIONS: Filling in the Blanks Read the excerpt and then answer the questions that follow.

Another European War?

Like piling thunderheads blanketing the whole horizon, last week a Great Debate took shape over the U.S. Could the U.S. keep out of Europe's war? Not for 20 years had U.S. citizens heard such ominous rumbling, not for 20 years had they searched the political skies with such anxiety. For they knew that, unless providentially the storm moved harmlessly on, the lightning issues of that debate would strike home to every man and woman in the nation.

Under that sky, political line-ups went by the board. The battle lines were drawn around a confused, mishandled, four-year-old Neutrality Act. To Washington the President summoned the Congress to meet on September 21 in special session. He prepared to ask them to repeal the major section of that act—the provision compelling him to declare absolute embargoes on the sale and shipment of arms and munitions to all countries at war.

Last week, before Congress met, up rose the ancient of the Senate, William Edgar Borah, to thwart the Presidential will. The knife-witted old (74) Lion of Idaho, symbol of romantic Lost Causes, took to the radio to tell the U.S. that repeal of the embargo meant taking sides in Europe, therefore intervention, therefore U.S. involvement in war. . . .

SOURCE: *Time* magazine, September 25, 1939.

1. Which war is being referred to as "Europe's war" in the article? _____

2. According to the article, why did President Franklin D. Roosevelt summon a special

session of Congress? _____

3. Why was the outcome of this special session so important? _____

_____

4. Does the article reflect the reporter's bias in any way? Cite examples to support your

opinion. _____

Activity
DIRECTIONS: Obtain a copy of a news magazine, such as *Time, Newsweek,* or *U.S. News and World Report*. Read the lead article and write a brief evaluation of the writer's objectivity. Suggest other sources that might verify the viewpoint of the article.

★ **Chapter Skills Activity 26**

Writing a Paragraph

A well-written paragraph includes a topic sentence stating the main idea of the paragraph, followed by sentences that expand on that idea by offering specific details. Details presented in a logical order, and transitional words or phrases linking sentences and ideas make the flow of ideas clear and easier for the reader to follow.

DIRECTIONS: Planning and Writing Paragraphs Determine a logical order for the sentences in A and B below and write the numbers of the sentences in the correct order on the lines. Underline the sentence in each group that would make a good topic sentence for a paragraph. Then use your answers as a plan and write a paragraph for A and B on a separate sheet of paper, using appropriate transitions to link ideas.

A. Benito Mussolini's Rise to Power

1. In 1922 the king of Italy declared Mussolini the head of the government.

2. Mussolini created widespread popular support for the ideas of fascism.

3. He rose to power by taking advantage of the resentment of Italians over the terms of the Versailles treaty.

4. He promised the Italian people that he would recapture the glory and might of ancient Rome.

5. Within a few years of gaining control of the government, Mussolini banned all political parties except the Fascist Party.

B. American Neutrality

1. In 1936 Congress approved legislation forbidding all loans to nations at war.

2. Congress passed a series of Neutrality Acts between 1935 and 1937.

3. European countries had still not repaid American loans made to them during World War I, and Congress wanted to avoid further debts.

4. The Neutrality Act of 1935 banned the sale of weapons to countries at war with one another.

5. The majority of Americans and government officials wanted to avoid becoming involved in international conflicts.

CRITICAL THINKING Review the paragraphs you wrote. Consider moving the topic sentence to a different place in the paragraph. In which position do you think the topic sentence is the most effective? Why?

Name _____ Date _____ Class _____

Using E-Mail

You can use a computer to communicate directly with another computer user through E-mail, or electronic mail. By entering a list of E-mail addresses, you can send the same message to many individuals or organizations that are connected to an E-mail network.

Friends who write back and forth used to be called "pen pals." Today they are called "key pals" because computer keyboards are used instead of pens. Find out what other students from around the world know about the cold war era. Have someone who has Internet access find the E-mail addresses of schools in the former Soviet Union or other European countries. One site, located at *www.web66.com* on the World Wide Web, lists school home pages from around the world, including two schools in St. Petersburg, Russia. Use these home pages to find E-mail addresses for the schools. With your classmates, write an E-mail letter to some of these schools. Introduce yourselves and share what you have learned about the cold war. Ask if students at the school would be willing to share what they know about this period.

DIRECTIONS: Analyzing Information Use what you learned about E-mail to answer the following questions.

1. What are some benefits in using E-mail rather than the regular postal service?

_____

2. Why do people use the term "key pal" instead of "pen pal"? _____

_____

3. How can you send the same letter to more than one location using E-mail?

_____

4. What is the difference between a school's home page and its E-mail address?

_____

Name _____ Date _____ Class _____

Using the Internet

If you have access to the Internet, you can explore a tremendous variety of research materials, from historical documents to the latest headlines from newspapers all around the world. Every day, hundreds of documents are added to the information available on the Internet.

DIRECTIONS: Exploring Space Flight History Using the Internet The National Aeronautics and Space Administration (NASA) has an Internet home page which connects to hundreds of pages dealing with space exploration. Start researching the history of space flight by loading the address, *www.nasa.gov*, into a Web browser. From there, follow the links on "Space Flight." Look for information on early space flight during the cold war era to answer the following questions.

1. What is the location bar on a Web page? _____

   _____

2. When you click your mouse cursor on some pictures, buttons, or underlined text,

   what happens? _____

   _____

3. Where is the Pathfinder satellite headed? _____

4. What was the name of the space capsule that carried Alan Shepard, Jr., into space?

   Where did you find this information? _____

   _____

★ **Chapter Skills Activity 29**

Drawing Conclusions

Whether you are reading a newspaper article or a science fiction story, you may need to read "between the lines" to understand the author's meaning. Authors do not always state their meaning directly. By considering the facts presented and using your own knowledge and insight, you can draw conclusions about an author's meaning.

DIRECTIONS: Filling in the Blanks The excerpt below is from a speech that Malcolm X made in Detroit in 1965. Read the excerpt and answer the questions below.

> "Now, what effect does [the struggle over Africa] have on us? Why should the black man in America concern himself since he's been away from the African continent for three or four hundred years? Why should we concern ourselves? What impact does what happens have upon us? Number one, you have to realize that up until 1959 Africa was dominated by the colonial powers. Having complete control over Africa, the colonial powers of Europe projected the image of Africa negatively . . . it was so negative that it was negative to you and me, and you and I began to hate it. We didn't want anybody telling us anything about Africa, much less calling us Africans. In hating Africa and in hating the Africans, we ended up hating ourselves, without even realizing it. Because you can't hate the roots of a tree, and not hate the tree. You can't hate your origin and not end up hating yourself. You can't hate Africa and not hate yourself."

1. What struggle in Africa was Malcolm X referring to in the first sentence? _____

_____

2. According to Malcolm X, why did many African Americans have a negative image

of themselves? _____

_____

3. Did Malcolm X believe that events in Africa should concern African Americans in the

United States? Why or why not? _____

_____

4. Why do you think Malcolm X believed that a more positive image of Africa was needed

to empower African Americans to fight for civil rights? _____

_____

★ **Chapter Skills Activity 30**

Building a Database

A computerized database program can help you organize and manage a large amount of information. Once you enter data in a database table, you can quickly locate a record according to key information. If you have a newspaper delivery route, for example, you could have the program list all your customers that live on a particular street. You could also locate all customers who receive newspapers on weekends only.

DIRECTIONS: Building a Database Table Research and use the information about the Vietnam War in the chapter to create a database of key events in the war from 1965 to 1973. Complete the database table below by filling in the year, key event or events, the number of United States troops in Vietnam that year, and the name of the United States president at the time. If figures are not given in the text, use the graph on page 860 in your textbook to get an estimate of troop strength.

Year	Event	President	Troop Strength
1965			
1966			
1967			
1968			
1969			
1970			
1971			
1972			
1973			

CRITICAL THINKING

If you specify the year as the key record, your data will automatically be displayed in chronological order by year. When might it be helpful to specify troop strength as the

key record? _____

★ **Chapter Skills Activity 31**

Predicting Consequences

Government officials make decisions based on how they think their policies and actions will affect the country and world. As a voter—whether in a school, local, or federal election—you will decide which candidate to support based on your own analysis of the likely consequences of a candidate's policies. Analyzing past events can help you make predictions about the impact of future policies, events, or decisions.

DIRECTIONS: Making Predictions The energy crisis of the 1970s affected American life in a number of ways. The chart below shows some of the short- and long-term effects of the energy crisis.

Effects of the Energy Crisis	
Short-Term Effects	**Long-Term Effects**
increase in price of gasoline	creation of U.S. Department of Energy
long lines at gas stations	research into alternative energy sources
gasoline rationing	changes in automobile design and technology
shortages of gasoline	laws requiring increase in energy efficiency of housing
feelings of frustration	public awareness of conservation

1. How do you think the energy crisis affected the daily lives of Americans?

_____

2. How do you think the energy crisis affected reliance on other forms of transportation

besides the automobile? _____

_____

3. Imagine that the United States discovered that its oil reserves were far less than what we believed they were. What effect would this discovery have? Think about its likely impact on individuals, businesses, government policy, and science and technology.

_____

4. Imagine that the United States discovered that its oil reserves were far greater than we believed they were. What effect do you think this discovery would have?

_____

_____

★ **Chapter Skills Activity 32**

Using an Electronic Spreadsheet

An electronic spreadsheet is the automated version of an accountant's ledger. It stores, manipulates, and displays numerical data. With only a few keystrokes on the computer, you can correct data, update data, and perform calculations.

DIRECTIONS: Entering Data in a Spreadsheet One of the major political issues in the 1990s has been the size of the federal deficit, or the amount by which government spending exceeds government revenues. Use the information in the table to the right to create a spreadsheet.

Federal Budget Summary: 1990–1996
(in millions of dollars)

| Year | Revenues | Government Expenditures | | |
		Human Resources	National Defense	Other
1990	1,031,321	619,329	277,331	333,855
1991	1,054,272	689,666	273,292	360,673
1992	1,090,453	772,440	298,350	310,066
1993	1,153,535	827,535	291,086	290,054
1994	1,257,737	869,414	281,642	309,785
1995	1,355,213	923,769	272,066	323,298
1996 (est.)	1,426,775	969,942	266,556	336,913

SOURCE: *Statistical Abstract of the United States.*

1. Enter the data from the table in the spreadsheet below.

2. Which cell shows human resources expenditures in 1992? _____

3. Enter a formula in the appropriate cells for calculating the total expenditures in each year.

4. Enter a formula in the appropriate cells for calculating the budget surplus or deficit for each year.

	A	B	C	D	E	F	G	H	I
1			1990	1991	1992	1993	1994	1995	1996
2	Revenues								
3	Expenditures								
4	Defense								
5	Human Resources								
6	Other								
7	Total								
8	Surplus/Deficit								
9									

Answer Key

★ ACTIVITY 1

1. a pueblo
2. Albuquerque
3. northeast
4. Isleta
5. 60 miles
6. Interstate highways are designed for long distance travel and often allow higher speed driving and amenities such as rest areas. Local and state roads often have traffic lights and intersections.

Activity: Students' maps will vary but should contain a reasonably accurate scale, compass rose, and location details.

★ ACTIVITY 2

1. 1000–1600
2. 100 years
3. in the Americas
4. in Europe
5. 88
6. after
7. Balboa discovered the Pacific Ocean.
8. The Black Death crushed Europe.

Activity: Time lines will vary but should show that the student understands how time lines are constructed.

★ ACTIVITY 3

1. the population of the American colonies
2. 1680 through 1730
3. 200,000
4. 1700
5. by about 80,000
6. by about 100,000–110,000
7. between 1720 and 1730
8. The population grew rapidly, with an increase in the rate of growth during the last two decades.

Activity: Bar graphs should accurately reflect the class attendance for the week.

★ ACTIVITY 4

CAUSES

1. differences in natural features, climate, and soil
2. Parliament wanted to make sure that only Great Britain profited from trade with the colonies.
3. rivalry between Great Britain and France
4. Farming was so profitable in the South.
5. The French were more tolerant than the British of Native American culture.

EFFECTS

1. The economies of the New England, Middle, and Southern Colonies developed differently.
2. Parliament passed laws controlling trade.
3. armed conflict between the French and the British
4. Agriculture formed the backbone of the Southern economy.
5. Many Native Americans fought on the side of the French.

Activity: Students' diagrams will vary. Some possible effects include not getting homework done; making parents angry; missing out on evening activities in order to complete homework. Students might add additional effects that grow out of their lists, such as not having homework done which might result in a failing grade, which might lower the grade for the grading period, and so on. Accept all reasonable chains of cause and effect.

⭐ ACTIVITY 5

1. **O**; should have
2. **F**; text of the Stamp Act
3. **O**; the most stirring
4. **O**; I think
5. **F**; text of speeches or other writings of colonial leaders
6. **F**; historical records of printing and sales of publications
7. **O**; probably would not have
8. **O**; the only
9. **F**; text of the pamphlet *Common Sense*

Activity: Letters will vary but should show that students understand that opinion statements are stronger and more persuasive when backed with facts.

⭐ ACTIVITY 6

1. New York, New Jersey, and Pennsylvania
2. a solid line and arrow
3. the south
4. the American forces
5. The British had a larger navy. Note that they sailed from New York to Chesapeake Bay, rather than taking a land route to Philadelphia.

Activity: Diary entries will vary but should show that students are able to use and project from the map.

⭐ ACTIVITY 7

1. Jefferson believes that educated citizens will preserve liberty because of their "good sense."
2. Madison believes that rule by the majority endangers individual liberty.
3. Both agreed that a bill of rights was necessary.
4. Jefferson
5. Madison

Activity: Students' charts will vary but should show evidence that students thought about various categories as criteria for comparison.

⭐ ACTIVITY 8

1. conflict between the United States and France
2. They began seizing American ships.
3. Adams sent negotiators to France.
4. The United States strengthened its military forces and prepared for war.
5. War broke out between Great Britain and France; British began to seize American ships; United States and Great Britain signed Jay's Treaty; France regarded Jay's Treaty as attempt by United States to aid Great Britain.

⭐ ACTIVITY 9

Students' answers will vary. Some important images in the poem include "the broad stripes and bright stars" of the flag, "the rockets' red glare," "the bombs bursting in air."

⭐ ACTIVITY 10

1. open
2. The water level is being raised. The open inlet valve allows water to flow into the lock.
3. The water level is higher in illustration 4.
4. The upper gate opens, allowing the boat to pass through the lock.

Activity: Diagrams will vary depending on the process students choose.

★ ACTIVITY 11

1. during the celebration of Andrew Jackson's inauguration in 1829

2. The writer of the piece was delayed in approaching the White House because of the crowds of people. Eventually, she gained entrance and was amazed at enormous, noisy crowds taking part in the celebration.

3. around and inside the White House

4. as "noisy and disorderly"

5. Students may infer that she was a member of the upper social class because of her condescending attitude toward "the people en masse" and her fear of "the people" as the most despotic of rulers.

Activity: Critiques will vary. Look for evidence of critical thinking about the source.

★ ACTIVITY 12

1. latitude 35°N, longitude 125°W

2. latitude 25°S, longitude 45°W

3. about 10 degrees

4. about 55 degrees

5. the Doldrums

Activity: Puzzles and answers will vary. Partners should provide feedback to each other about the solutions to the puzzles.

★ ACTIVITY 13

1. the proportion of people living in rural areas to people living in urban areas from 1830 to 1860

2. 91 percent; 80 percent

3. 1840–1850; 1830–1860

4. Although a far greater percentage of people lived in rural areas than in urban areas in 1830–1860, the percentage of people living in urban areas was steadily increasing.

Activity: Circle graphs should accurately reflect the makeup of the class.

★ ACTIVITY 14

1. 46 items

2. press "Enter"

3. *Get on Board: The Story of the Underground Railroad*

4. type "5"

5. "B" for "Back"

6. "SO" for "Start Over"

Activity: Students' catalog screens and book descriptions will vary. Look for evidence of accurate research.

★ ACTIVITY 15

Students' answers may vary. Possible answers include:

1. They felt satisfied with their lives and performed their work willingly.

2. They never rebelled or even appeared to be dissatisfied; they obeyed the writer's grandfather "implicitly."

3. She presents a positive view of slavery.

4. Her grandfather was a slaveholder, and her writing reflects admiration for him.

5. The author does not state her bias directly, but her failure to consider slavery as a moral issue indicates her bias.

★ ACTIVITY 16

1. Map Index and/or Multimedia Maps

2. Sound Index

3. Print

4. Type in Civil War, Europe and click on search.

5. Type in casualties, Gettysburg and click on search.

6. Type in African Americans, Union army and click on search.

◼ ACTIVITY 17

1. the condition of the newly freed African Americans

2. They have almost no education, knowledge of business, or skills. Few of them are mechanics and none of them are skilled manufacturers; they do not own property.

3. War may break out between the races.

4. The United States government must give the former slaves land and money with which they can begin to build independent lives.

5. Students' answers will vary. Their suggested main ideas should make sense in light of their readings in the textbook and the information presented in the reading.

◼ ACTIVITY 18

1. It shows Native American reservations in the West in 1890.

2. the Indian Territory which later became the state of Oklahoma

3. Walla Walla and Shoshone

4. By 1890 these territories had not yet been admitted to the Union as states.

5. Answers will vary but may include that the government wanted Native Americans to settle down and become farmers. The reservations were often on poor or dry land that white settlers did not want. Some people may have felt that the Native Americans could be more easily controlled on reservations; others may have felt that the Native Americans could be protected on reservations.

◼ ACTIVITY 19

1. New York: 5 P.M.; London: 10 P.M.; Moscow: 1 A.M.

2. 4 hours

3. 4 hours

4. The boundaries of some time zones are adjusted for convenience. For example, it would be inconvenient if only a small part of a state or country were in a different time zone from the rest of the state or country.

◼ ACTIVITY 20

1. the production of steel ingots and castings

2. 1875–1900

3. 1890

4. about 10 million

5. 1895–1900

6. The economy was becoming more industrialized.

Activity: Line graphs will vary depending on the subject students choose. Look for evidence that students understand the process of creating line graphs.

◼ ACTIVITY 21

1. a coal trust; the common people

2. the coal trust is squeezing him

3. The difference in size represents the enormous power the coal trust has over the people.

4. The figure representing the coal trust is well-dressed, wearing trousers with gold buttons on the side and an elaborate hat with a feather, and he is adding coins to his already full bags of money.

5. It is still rising.

6. The cartoonist believes that coal trusts are greedy and indifferent to the common people. He probably feels the same about big business in general.

Activity: Students' cartoons will vary depending on the issue students choose.

✦ ACTIVITY 22

Students' answers will vary. Check that students have included a variety of resources that would enhance their presentations.

Activity: Students' multimedia presentations will vary.

✦ ACTIVITY 23

Some answers may vary. Possible answers are given.

I.
  A.
    1. made up of business, labor, and public representatives
    2. pressured businesses to grant workers' demands in return for agreement not to strike
  B.
    1. result of large numbers of men in armed forces
    2.
      a. women hired for jobs previously held by men
      b. migration of African Americans to Northern cities
      c. migration of Mexicans to the United States
  C.
    1. sale of Liberty Bonds
    2. tax increases
  D.
    1.
      a. sought to persuade Americans of necessity of fighting war
      b. distributed pamphlets and advertisements and organized speeches
      c. greatest propaganda campaign in United States history

II.
  A.
    1. headed by Herbert Hoover
    2. aimed to increase production and encourage conservation

III.
  A. boost for American economy
  B. created atmosphere for intolerance of "different" ideas
  C.
    1. known as "Great Migration"
    2. headed north to find jobs
    3. race riots in several Northern cities

IV.
  A.
    1. majority of Americans opposed involvement at first
    2. German Americans, Irish Americans, socialists, and pacifists remained opposed
    3. strong opposition from women's groups
  B.
    1. Committee on Public Information tried to suppress dissent
    2. Congress passed Espionage, Sabotage, and Sedition Acts

✦ ACTIVITY 24

1. invalid
2. valid
3. valid
4. invalid
5. Americans pursued new leisure activities with enthusiasm.

Activity: Students' generalizations will vary depending on the local newspaper chosen. Look for evidence to support students' conclusions.

■ ACTIVITY 25

1. World War II

2. He wanted Congress to repeal the provision of the Neutrality Act that called for a complete embargo on the sale and shipment of arms to Europe.

3. A repeal of the embargo would almost certainly lead to United States involvement in World War II.

4. Answers will vary. The reporter presented both sides of the argument, but some students may find the characterization of Senator Borah biased.

Activity: Students' evaluations will vary depending on the source they choose for their evaluation. Look for evidence to support their conclusions.

■ ACTIVITY 26

Answers will vary. Suggested order of sentences:

A. 2, 3, 1, 5, 4; Topic sentence: 2

B. 5, 3, 2, 4, 1; Topic sentence: 5

Critical Thinking: Students' evaluations of the position of the topic sentence may vary. Possible positions include the beginning of the paragraph because it guides the reader or at the end because it summarizes the materials used to support the ideas in the paragraph.

■ ACTIVITY 27

1. E-mail is faster to send because you do not have to travel to a mailbox to send it, and it is usually delivered in minutes. It is also less expensive in most cases, and it is more convenient because one message can be sent to several different addresses without using stamps and envelopes.

2. "Key pal" is used because people communicate using computer keys to write messages instead of pens.

3. Simply type each address into multiple "to" boxes above the message.

4. A school's home page is a place where information, including text and pictures is located on the Internet. An E-mail address is a place that cannot be seen or read like a home page. Instead it is a location where messages are received.

■ ACTIVITY 28

1. This bar shows the address of the currently displayed page after it is fully loaded.

2. A new page of information is loaded for viewing.

3. Mars

4. Freedom 7; this information is found on a page listing flights of Project Mercury which is reached by following links dealing with human space flights.

■ ACTIVITY 29

1. the struggle of Africans against colonial dominance

2. He believed that the colonial powers of Europe had created a negative image of Africans and that caused African Americans to think negatively about themselves.

3. He believed that the African American people in the United States should be concerned about the African struggle because their origins were in Africa.

4. Answers will vary, but students might say that a more positive image of Africa would increase self-esteem among African Americans and allow them to fight for their rights.

★ ACTIVITY 30

Events chosen for inclusion may vary. Sample answers are given.

1965: Johnson begins to escalate United States involvement; Johnson; 180,000

1966: Fulbright hearings on war; Johnson; 400,000

1967: Stennis hearings on war; Johnson; 490,000

1968: Tet offensive; Johnson; 510,000

1969: Withdrawal of troops begins; Nixon; 485,000

1970: Invasion of Cambodia; Nixon; 334,000

1971: Nikita Khrushchev dies of heart attack in Russia; Nixon; 60,000

1972: "Christmas bombing" of North Vietnam; Nixon; 10,000

1973: Peace agreement signed; Nixon; 5,000

Critical Thinking: It would be helpful to display records by troop strength to locate quickly the year of greatest or lowest troop strength or to see patterns in troop buildup.

★ ACTIVITY 31

Answers will vary. Sample answers are given.

1. Americans planned errands carefully to use a minimum of gasoline; they changed vacation plans; they formed car pools for commuting.

2. Bicycles became popular during the 1970s; more people relied on mass transportation; government funded the expansion of mass transportation.

3. Price increases and rationing would probably result; people would reduce their energy consumption through a combination of voluntary and government imposed measures; the federal government and local communities might support increased reliance on nuclear energy and establish more mass transit systems; the government would finance more research into other sources of energy that are now considered impractical or too costly.

4. An unexpected increase in energy resources would probably increase people's consumption and cause a drop in prices. However, increases in consumption might not be as great as expected because of the profound impact that the energy crisis had on society's awareness of natural resources and the environment.

★ ACTIVITY 32

1. Check students' spreadsheets.

2. E5

3. Example: In cell C7, the formula "C4 + C5 + C6" should be entered to calculate total expenditures for 1990.

4. Example: in cell C8, the formula "C2 − C7" should be entered to calculate budget deficit for 1990.